Young INDIANA in THE CURSE OF KHA

Hippo MYSTERY ? PUZZLES

Owen Williams

Illustrated by Paddy Mounter

Hippo

Scholastic Children's Books,
Scholastic Publications Ltd,
7-9 Pratt Street, London NW1 OAE, UK

Scholastic Inc.,
730 Broadway, New York, NY 10003, USA

Scholastic Canada Ltd,
123 Newkirk Road, Richmond Hill,
Ontario L4C 3G5, Canada

Ashton Scholastic Pty Ltd,
P O Box 579, Gosford, New South Wales,
Australia

Ashton Scholastic Ltd,
Private Bag 1, Penrose, Auckland,
New Zealand

™ *and* © Lucasfilm Ltd. All Rights Reserved. Scholastic Publications
Authorised User.

First published by Scholastic Publications Ltd, 1993

Text copyright © Owen Williams, 1993

Illustrations copyright © Paddy Mounter, 1993

ISBN 0 590 55087 X

Printed in Belgium by Proost International Book Production

THE JOURNEY BEGINS

IN THE YEAR 1908 THE JONES FAMILY SETS SAIL FROM AMERICA FOR A LECTURE TOUR OF EUROPE. AS THE MAGNIFICENT LINER STEAMS OUT OF NEW YORK HARBOUR, YOUNG INDIANA JONES EXCITEDLY WAVES GOODBYE AND WONDERS WHAT ADVENTURES LIE IN STORE FOR HIM.

THEY CRUISE EFFORTLESSLY ACROSS THE ATLANTIC BEFORE STOPPING IN ENGLAND TO EMPLOY MISS SEYMOUR AS INDY'S GOVERNESS. THEN THEY CHANGE BOATS AND CONTINUE ON THEIR LONG JOURNEY.

GOODBYE AMERICA!

NEW YORK

LONDON

ALEXANDRIA

A FEW WEEKS LATER THEY REACH THEIR SECOND PORT OF CALL...

6

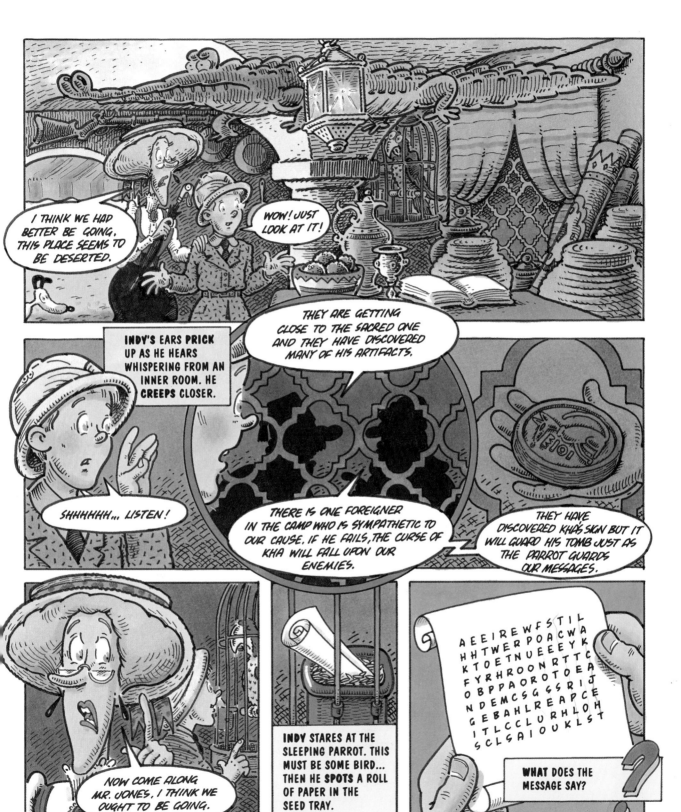

7

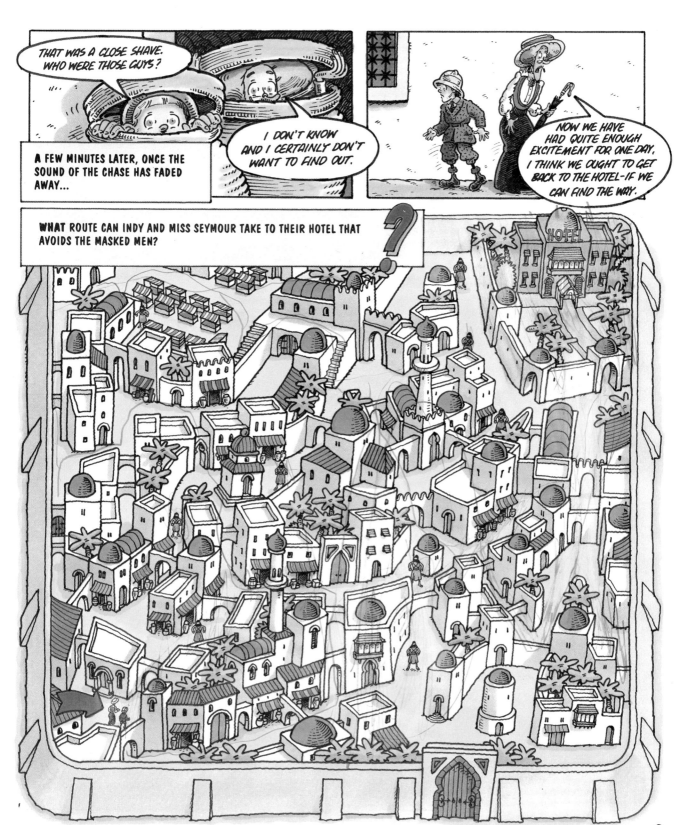

THE NEXT MORNING IS SPENT STUDYING IN THE HOTEL UNDER MISS SEYMOUR'S EAGLE EYE. BUT AFTER LUNCH AN ARCHAEOLOGICAL EXPEDITION IS ORGANIZED — IT IS TIME FOR A CAMEL RIDE TO THE PYRAMIDS.

ARE YOU SURE 100 PIASTRES WAS ENOUGH? HE WANTED 300.

THESE PEOPLE EXPECT TO BARTER YOU KNOW, HE'LL BE PERFECTLY CONTENT BY THE TIME WE GET DOWN. NOW, LET'S GET ON.

@#$%!!⚡☠!!

THEY CLIMB UP...

THIS PYRAMID WAS BUILT OVER 4000 YEARS AGO.

BY KING CHEOPS - FOURTH DYNASTY.

...AND UP...

VERY GOOD. IT WAS THE LARGEST CONSTRUCTION MADE BY MAN AND WAS ONE OF THE WONDERS OF THE WORLD.

I GUESS KING CHEOPS WAS PRETTY OLD BY THE TIME IT WAS FINISHED.

...AND UP...

SOME PHARAOHS, LIKE RAMESES THE SECOND, LIVED TO BE OVER NINETY BUT OTHERS WERE ONLY BOYS WHEN THEY DIED.

YOU MEAN MY AGE MISS SEYMOUR?

NED TAKES CHARGE AND WHEN DARKNESS FALLS THEY ARE SITTING AROUND A FLICKERING FIRE LISTENING TO NED'S STORIES.

WHEN YOU OPEN A TOMB IT'S AS IF TIME HAS STOOD STILL. LIGHT PIERCES THE DARKNESS FOR THE FIRST TIME IN THOUSANDS OF YEARS...

YOU MAY FIND FOOTPRINTS OF MEN WHO LAID THE MUMMY TO REST...

OR FINGERPRINTS OF AN EGYPTIAN PAINTER ON A PLASTER WALL.

GOLLEE!! THAT SOUNDS GREAT. MAYBE I'LL FIND A TOMB FULL OF TREASURE, THEN I'LL BE RICH.

NO HENRY. ARCHAEOLOGY DOESN'T STEAL FROM THE PAST, IT OPENS UP ITS TREASURES AND SECRETS TO EVERYONE.

NED TELLS THEM THAT HE IS GOING UP RIVER IN THE MORNING ABOARD A DHOW. HE HAS A FRIEND WORKING ON HOWARD CARTER'S DIG.

WOULD YOU LIKE TO COME?

WOW!! I'M SURE MY PARENTS WILL SAY YES! CAN WE GO MISS SEYMOUR- CAN WE?

WE SHALL HAVE TO WAIT AND SEE, HENRY.

WELL IF YOU CAN MAKE IT I'LL BE ON CAPTAIN PATCH'S DHOW FIRST THING IN THE MORNING, NOW I HAVE SOME SPARE BLANKETS, WE OUGHT TO GET SOME SLEEP.

THE NEXT MORNING... INDY PERSUADES HIS PARENTS TO LET HIM GO. SOON AFTER DAWN THEY MAKE THEIR WAY TO THE WATERFRONT.

WELL HERE WE ARE MISS SEYMOUR, BUT THERE'S NO SIGN OF NED.

CAN YOU SPOT NED'S DHOW?

HELLO THERE! GLAD YOU COULD MAKE IT.

WELCOME ABOARD, I'LL TAKE THE BAGS. THERE'S A FEW MINUTES BEFORE WE CAST OFF — SHALL WE INVESTIGATE THE SHIP?

BUT THERE IS NO ARGUING WITH MISS SEYMOUR. INDY TRIES TO CONCENTRATE WHILE ROPES ARE CAST OFF, THE SAIL IS HOISTED AND THE JOURNEY BEGINS.

I THINK HENRY SHOULD INVESTIGATE HIS HISTORY BOOK FIRST, CHAPTER THREE — NAPOLEON.

INDY FINDS IT HARD TO READ AS THEY DRIFT DOWN THE EVER-CHANGING NILE.

THEN A SHADOW FALLS OVER HIM AND **SOMETHING** THAT COULD BE THE END OF AN UMBRELLA POKES HIM IN THE BACK.

OOOOOHH!! ER! ...SORRY MISS SEYMOUR, I WAS JUST...

GASP!!

عشان كوبرسلاق
عحريشسايتلاكيتو
شايتبكاتي ؟؟

DON'T WORRY, THEY ONLY WANT TO KNOW WHAT YOU'RE READING. THE ARABS ARE VERY INTERESTED IN LEARNING. I'LL TALK TO THEM.

NED TALKS TO THE CREW IN ARABIC. INDY IS IMPRESSED.

RASHID SHOWS THEM TO THE TENT INTO WHICH HOWARD CARTER HAS JUST STEPPED.

THIS IS MR. CARTER'S TENT. PLEASE COME IN.

AHHHHHH!!

SORRY ABOUT THAT OLD CHAP- HOW DO YOU DO.?

AS INDY WALKS INTO THE TENT HE IS **STARTLED** BY A PHOTOGRAPHER'S MAGNESIUM FLASH. MISS SEYMOUR SITS HIM DOWN IN A CHAIR WHILE HOWARD CARTER INTRODUCES HIMSELF TO THE GROUP AND APOLOGIZES TO INDY.

THIS IS PIERRE, OUR OFFICIAL PHOTOGRAPHER. WE LIKE TO HAVE A PHOTOGRAPHIC RECORD OF ALL OUR FINDS.

OUR EXCAVATIONS HAVE UNEARTHED ALL MANNER OF ARTIFACTS...POTTERY...LINEN...CLAY TABLETS... THE ONE YOU'RE HOLDING BEARS THE IMAGE OF TUTANKHAMUN.

THE BOY-PHARAOH! HOW OLD WAS HE ?

CARTER TELLS INDY THAT TUTANKHAMUN WAS ONLY ABOUT EIGHTEEN WHEN HE DIED.

I AM SURE WE ARE CLOSE TO HIS TOMB. I AM DETERMINED TO FIND IT.

AND THE TOMB YOU FOUND YESTERDAY?

IT IS THE TOMB OF A MAN NAMED KHA. HE WAS SOME KIND OF ARCHITECT OR ENGINEER. WE WILL KNOW MORE WHEN WE OPEN THE TOMB. WOULD YOU LIKE TO COME ALONG ?

18

19

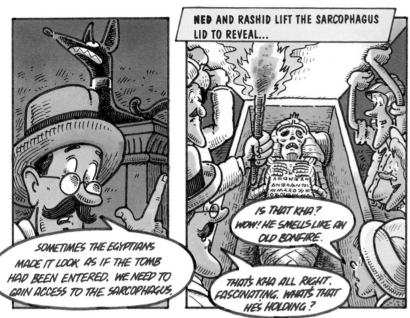

AS NED'S BOOTS HIT THE LAST STONE THEY HEAR A **RUMBLING** DEEP UNDERGROUND.

NED HAS SOLVED THE RIDDLE AND IS **BOUNDING** FROM STONE TO STONE BEFORE ANYONE CAN STOP HIM. ALL THEY CAN DO IS HOLD THEIR BREATH.

RUMBLE!! RUMBLE!!

WHATEVER THAT NOISE WAS IT'S MADE THE FLOOR SAFE. YOU CAN COME ACROSS NOW.

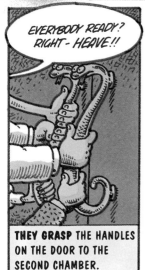

EVERYBODY READY? RIGHT - HEAVE!!

THEY GRASP THE HANDLES ON THE DOOR TO THE SECOND CHAMBER.

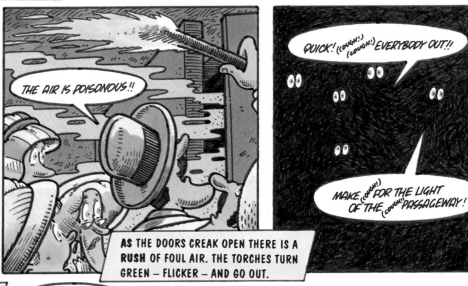

THE AIR IS POISONOUS!!

QUICK! (COUGH!) (COUGH!) EVERYBODY OUT!!

MAKE (COUGH!) FOR THE LIGHT OF THE (COUGH!) PASSAGEWAY!

AS THE DOORS CREAK OPEN THERE IS A **RUSH** OF FOUL AIR. THE TORCHES TURN GREEN — FLICKER — AND GO OUT.

COUGHING, EYES STREAMING, THEY **STUMBLE** OUT OF THE TOMB AND INTO THE FRESH AIR.

THANK GOODNESS EVERYONE IS SAFE.

YES. WE'LL GO BACK IN THE MORNING BUT WE'LL NEED A GUARD TONIGHT.

I WILL GUARD THE TOMB MYSELF MR. CARTER.

GOOD MAN. I'M SURE THERE'S NO DANGER BUT TAKE MY REVOLVER, JUST IN CASE.

NIGHT FALLS AND THE RISING MOON FINDS RASHID ON GUARD...

JACKALS HOWLING...

INDY SNORING...

UNTIL JUST AFTER DAWN...

23

24

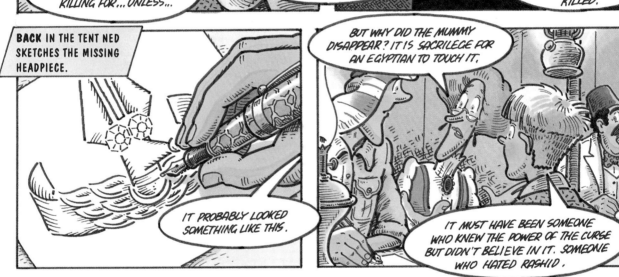

26

IT'S THE POWDER I FOUND ON RASHID'S BODY...

... I WONDER.

NED POURS OUT THE POWDER.

POOFF!

PHOTOGRAPHER'S FLASH POWDER!!

PIERRE!!

I KNOW WHAT YOU'RE THINKING, BUT WE CAN'T DO ANYTHING TONIGHT. WE'LL SEE WHAT WE CAN FIND OUT IN THE MORNING.

ZZZZZZZZZZ!!

AS DAWN IS BREAKING, A SHADOWY FIGURE ENTERS INDY'S TENT.

DON'T BE ALARMED OLD CHAP, IT'S ONLY ME. I NEED YOUR HELP.

NED?

I'M GOING TO SEARCH PIERRE'S TENT. LOOK, YOU CAN JUST SEE HIM FROM HERE. IF HE MOVES, COME AND TELL ME — QUICK.

OK NED, YOU CAN COUNT ON ME.

INDY ONLY LOOKS AWAY FOR A FEW SHORT MOMENTS

BUT BY THE TIME HE IS READY, PIERRE HAS DISAPPEARED.

I MUST GO AFTER HIM! BUT WHICH TRACKS SHOULD I FOLLOW?

CAN YOU WORK OUT WHICH SET OF FOOTPRINTS INDY SHOULD FOLLOW?

27

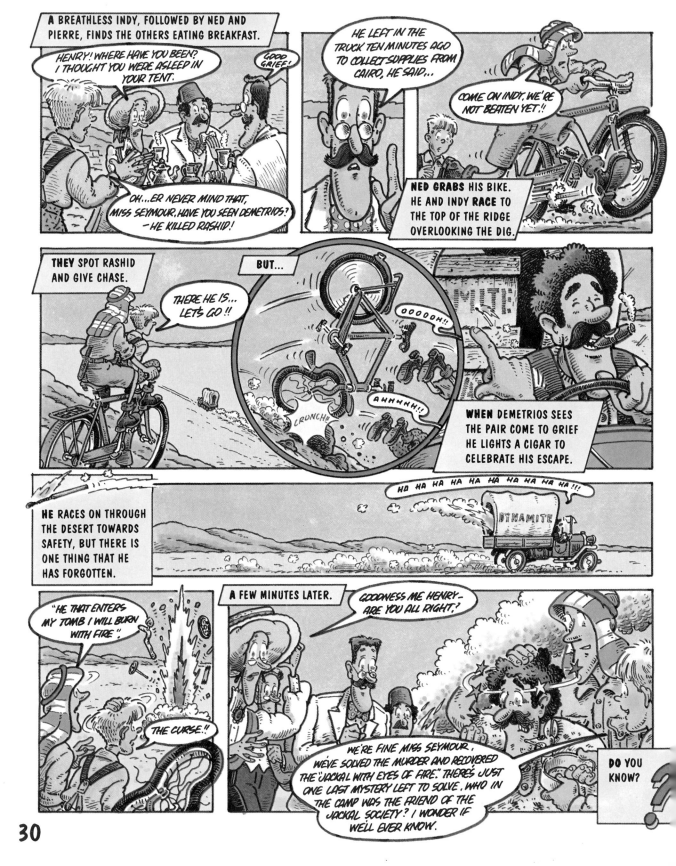

30

ANSWERS

PAGES 4/5
THIS MAN DROPPED THE WALLET.

HERE HE IS NOW.

PAGES 6/7
TO DECODE THE MESSAGE BEGIN WITH THE LETTER AT THE BOTTOM RIGHT HAND CORNER OF THE PIECE OF PAPER AND READ UPWARDS. MOVE TO THE NEXT COLUMN OF LETTERS ON THE LEFT AND REPEAT THIS METHOD UNTIL THE END OF THE MESSAGE.

THE MESSAGE SAYS: THE JACKAL SOCIETY WILL PROTECT KHA'S TREASURES. ONE OF OUR GROUP WILL SOON REACH CARTER'S CAMP. HE WILL BE PROTECTED BY THE SIGN OF KHA.

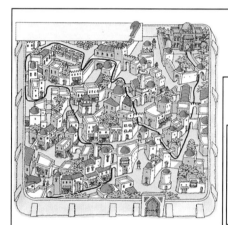

PAGES 8/9
THE SAFE ROUTE BACK TO THE HOTEL IS MARKED IN BLACK.

PAGES 10/11
IF YOU LOOK CAREFULLY AT THE PYRAMID YOU SHOULD BE ABLE TO MAKE OUT THE SHADOW OF A FIGURE ON A BICYCLE.

PAGES 12/13
NED WILL BE ON THIS DHOW. HIS BICYCLE IS BEING LOADED ONTO IT.

PAGES 14/15
THE ROUTE TO THE CAMP IS MARKED IN BLACK.

PAGES 16/17
THIS IS HOWARD CARTER. YOU CAN RECOGNIZE HIM FROM HIS PHOTOGRAPH IN THE NEWSPAPER CUTTING ON PAGE 6.

PAGES 18/19
INDY HAS NOTICED THIS ARTIFACT. HE SAW A SIMILAR ONE IN THE JACKAL SOCIETY'S HQ.

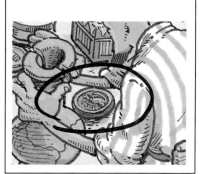

PAGES 20/21
THE SAFE ROUTE ACROSS THE FLOOR IS MARKED IN BLACK.

PAGES 22/23
THE DIFFERENCES IN THE TOMB ARE CIRCLED IN THIS PICTURE.

1. HANDLE MISSING FROM VASE.
2. COFFIN LID HAS MOVED.
3. BODY IS LYING HERE.

WHAT DO YOU THINK HAS HAPPENED?

PAGES 24/25
THE INSCRIPTION SAYS: THE PHARAOH GAVE ME A PRECIOUS HEADPIECE — THE SACRED JACKAL WITH EYES OF FIRE.

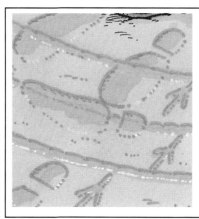

PAGES 26/27
INDY SAW PIERRE WITH HIS CAMERA AND TRIPOD. THIS TRAIL WAS MADE BY PIERRE DRAGGING THE TRIPOD OVER THE SAND.

PAGES 28/29
INDY HAS SPOTTED THREE GIVE-AWAY CLUES.

1. A SET OF FOOTPRINTS.
2. A CIGAR BUTT.
3. THE DETONATOR HANDLE.

ALL THIS EVIDENCE POINTS TO DEMETRIOS (SEE THE PICTURE OF DEMETRIOS ON PAGE 17). HE KILLED RASHID AND TRIED TO BLAME IT ON THE CURSE OF KHA.

PAGE 30
NED IS THE FRIEND OF THE JACKAL SOCIETY. YOU CAN SEE THE JACKAL SIGN ON HIS DAGGER AND HIS BAG. HE JOINED THE SOCIETY TO PROTECT THE EGYPTIANS' ARCHAEOLOGICAL TREASURES FROM THIEVES.